ABC
OF
(not too) # NATURAL
HISTORY

by
"Gramps" (a.k.a. Francis Hardesty)
and Mary Ann Ross

ISBN: 979-8-9853351-5-6 (paperback)

ISBN: 979-8-9853351-6-3 (hard cover)

Mary Ann Ross
guymaross@yahoo.com

Additional copies may be purchased through:
Marla Jones, Book Design
405.354.7422

Photos courtesy of Pixabay

Dedicated to all grandparents who love and nurture their grandchildren, like my grandfather did.

Mary Ann Hardesty Ross

This book was written over 75 years ago, therefore it contains unusual and outdated words and sayings. Despite the discrepancies of time and social practices, this book remains a beautiful piece of historical literature. The author's granddaughter has added color photos to update the book for today's young readers. We hope you enjoy this whimsical visit to the past.

He
wo
th

Beetles are bugs often found in trees.

They fly through the air with the greatest of ease.

And when they're not flying, they'll carefully pack

Their wings in the cases they tote on their back.

C

Crickets, they tell me, can't talk, sing, or yell.

They do make a noise and they do it quite well!

They chirp!

(and I'm told that they foretell the weather)

And they do it by rubbing their hind legs together.

cricket

WEATHER
FORECAST
AM.
PM.

D d

Doodlebugs live in little round pits

Where right in the middle the doodlebug sits.

And should an ant or such fall to the bottom,

The doodlebug up and yells,

"Yippee! I got 'em!"

ant lion, aka doodlebug

emu

Emus are birds and all birds have wings.

But emus never make use of the things!

They travel on foot as fast as a breeze.

They scamper along with the greatest of ease.

Fleas are among the most agile of all
Though a flea, an insect, is really quite small.
If a flea was as big as even a mouse,
He'd be able to jump right over your house!

flea

grasshopper

Grasshoppers hop. (Now isn't that silly!)

They hop and hop until the weather gets chilly.

They hop in the summer, night and day I suppose.

But not in the winter 'cause their hoppers get froze!

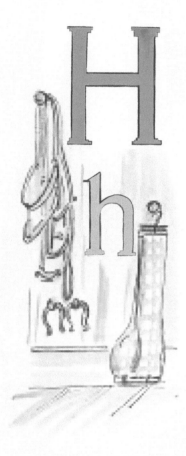

horse

Horses are creatures that wear iron shoes.

You see them in farmyards but seldom in zoos.

They trot and they canter, they gallop and prance.

They often wear saddles, but never wear pants!

I i

ibex

An io and ibex are quite different you'll note.

The io's a moth, the ibex, a goat...

A goat with thick hair and long crooked horns.

It never wears shoes, so it never gets corns.

J j

donkeys

Jackasses really have four legs, not two.

And one never knows what a jackass will do.

When jackasses sing, they think they're okay.

But four legs or two,

it's just a loud

br-a-y !

Kangaroos never, from what I have read,

Play tunes on an oboe, or have breakfast in bed.

If her baby is sleepy, Mama won't rock it

She'll tuck baby into her nice, cozy pocket.

kangaroo

lobster

Lobsters are shellfish with big, ugly nippers.

They never wear mittens or vests with zippers.

Lobsters can't blush, but their faces get red

When too long in the sunshine, so my grandmother said.

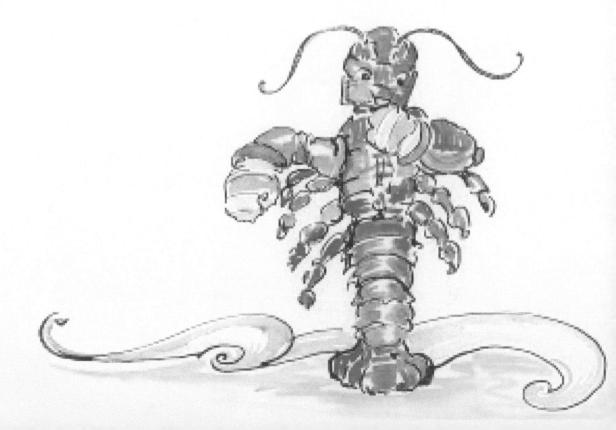

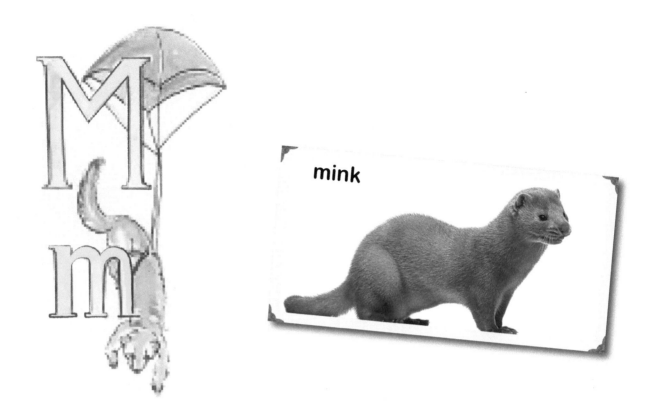

mink

Mink are long animals, not very tall.

And so when they tumble, they've not far to fall.

Ladies use their fur to keep out the cold

And this keeps the minks from getting too old.

weevil

Nut weevils are insects and start life in a nut.

You'd think they'd be crazy—

—they're anything but!

They eat up the kernel and live in the shell

Which keeps out the weather, and does it quite well!

owl

Owls are the night birds who are supposed to be wise,

'Cause they keep shut their mouths and keep open their eyes.

But if they are wise would they do as they do?

Would they sit up all night saying nothing but **WHOOOO**...

WHOO...

WHOO ?

people

People are animals—funny ones, too!

They often do things they oughtn't to do.

People wear clothes held by hook, pin, or button

While all other animals never wear nothin'!

quagga*

Quaggas are animals much like our donkeys.

They live in South Africa, same as the monkeys.

A quagga is speedy. When he travels, he scoots!

But he'd not be so fast if he had to wear boots.

*Quaggas, a subspecies of zebra, are now extinct.

R r

Reindeer are animals used by the Lapps,

The Eskimos, too, and Old Santa perhaps.

They live in the north with its ice, cold, and snow.

Could they live in the south? I just wouldn't know.

reindeer

shark

Sharks are fish that are found in the sea.

They've been known to bite, but they never bit me.

They have awful rough skin from life in the ocean.

If I knew a shark, I'd get him some lotion.

tadpole

Tadpoles are frogs whose legs haven't grown,

While frogs are old tadpoles with legs of their own.

A tadpole is really a very nice fellow.

But great big frogs just sit 'round and

b-e-ll-ow...

unicorn

Unicorns, hmmmm... I've heard it said

They are quite like a horse with a horn on its head.

But no one I've known since the time I was born,

Has ever yet seen a live unicorn.

vole

Voles are small, "field mice" to you.

They nest in the grass like the bumblebees do.

They pester the farmer and ruin his crops.

They'd rather eat corn than eat lollipops!

woodchuck

Woodchucks are animals that do not grow big.

They're often called "groundhog"—

but never "groundpig"!

They wake in the spring and come out to peek.

And if they see shadows?

It's six weeks more sleep!

Xiphias are fishes—well what do you know!

I'd never have thought it, but really, it's so—

Fish that carry a sword on the nose,

Some call them swordfish.

Why do you suppose?

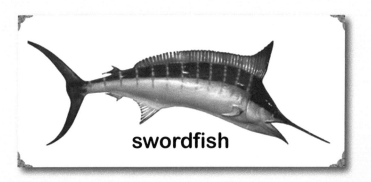

swordfish

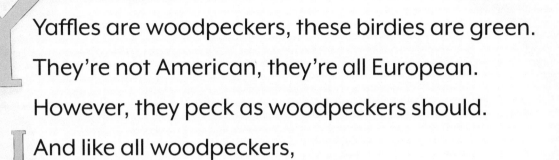

Yaffles are woodpeckers, these birdies are green.

They're not American, they're all European.

However, they peck as woodpeckers should.

And like all woodpeckers,

they

peck

holes

in

wood.

woodpecker

Z z

Zebras resemble the horse quite a lot.

But zebras are striped, and horses are not.

They're white with black striping.

They are a sight!

While others insist they are

black striped with **white!**

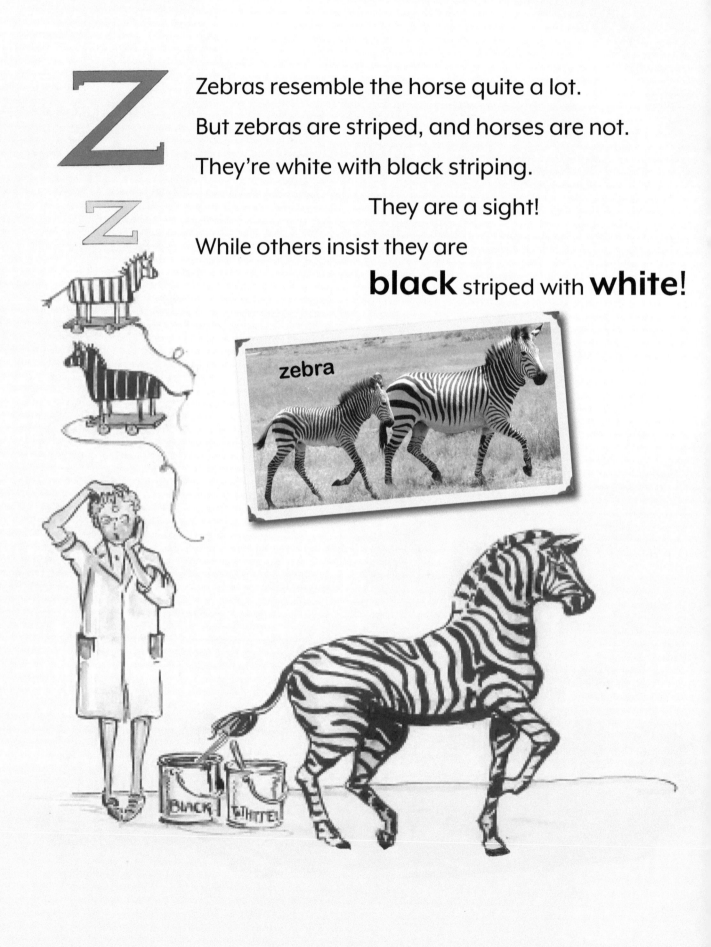

zebra

I hope you enjoyed my grandfather's book with the different kinds of animals! You can read Gramps' silly book over and over, and love it again and again, just like I do.

Meet the Authors

Francis DeGrotte Hardesty was born in the state of Virginia in the year 1884. That's over 130 years ago! He graduated as a captain from an elite military school called Virginia Tech Corps of Cadets. He became a lawyer, helping people patent their inventions.

Hardesty enjoyed writing poetry for his own enjoyment. He loved his grandchildren and always talked about funny things with them. This book shows just how humorous and clever he was!

Francis DeGrotte Hardesty

Mary Ann Hardesty Ross

Mary Ann Hardesty Ross was one year old when her grandfather, Francis Hardesty, wrote this book for her. Mary Ann read the book over and over as a child then tucked it away in a box for safekeeping. Mary Ann has updated the book so she can share it with young children of today.

Ross is an Okie from Muskogee, Oklahoma. She went to college at Oklahoma Christian University. Mary Ann taught multiple ages, from preschool to adult; as well as English as a Second Language (ESL) in Edmond, Oklahoma. Ross has been married fifty-seven years to Guy Ross. They have three children (one is deceased) and six grandchildren.

CPSIA information can be obtained
at www.ICGtesting.com
Printed in the USA
BVHW021422270622
640734BV00006B/6